Ladybird Readers

Playing Football

D0412812

Series Editor: Sorrel Pitts
Text adapted by Sorrel Pitts

LADYBIRD BOOKS

UK | USA | Canada | Ireland | Australia
India | New Zealand | South Africa

Ladybird Books is part of the Penguin Random House group of companies
whose addresses can be found at global.penguinrandomhouse.com.
www.penguin.co.uk   www.puffin.co.uk   www.ladybird.co.uk

Text adapted from 'Peppa Pig: Playing Football' - Read it Yourself with Ladybird,
first published by Ladybird Books 2016
This version published by Ladybird Books 2018
001

This book is based on the
TV Series 'Peppa Pig'.
'Peppa Pig' is created by
Neville Astley and Mark Baker.
Peppa Pig © Astley Baker Davies Ltd/
Entertainment One UK Ltd 2003.

www.peppapig.com

Printed in China

A CIP catalogue record for this book is available from the British Library

ISBN: 978-0-241-31947-5

All correspondence to:
Ladybird Books
Penguin Random House Children's
80 Strand, London WC2R 0RL

Ladybird Readers

Playing Football

Based on the Peppa Pig
TV series

Picture words

Peppa

Daddy Pig

Pedro
Pony

Suzy
Sheep

Danny
Dog

Rebecca
Rabbit

Richard
Rabbit

teams

goalkeeper

goal

Peppa and Suzy Sheep
played tennis.

"I'm hitting the ball to
you, Peppa!" said Suzy.

"I'm hitting the ball to
you, Suzy!" said Peppa.

George wanted to play tennis, too.

"You can't play tennis, George," said Peppa, "but you can get the ball for me and Suzy."

Peppa and Suzy loved
playing tennis.

"Get the ball, George!"
said Peppa.

George had to get the ball.
He ran and ran.

George did not love tennis.

Peppa's friends came.
They wanted to play, too.

"We can play football!"
said Danny Dog.

"Great!" the children said.

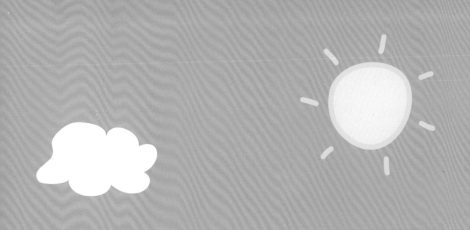

The friends were in teams.
There was a boys' team
and a girls' team.

Pedro Pony was the
goalkeeper for the boys' team.
Rebecca Rabbit was the
goalkeeper for the girls' team.

Richard Rabbit got
the ball. He ran and ran.

He kicked the ball past
Peppa and Suzy . . .

Then, Richard kicked the ball past Rebecca, and into the goal!

"Great!" said the boys.

19

Rebecca got the ball.
Then, she threw it into
the goal.

"Great!" said the girls.

"You can't do that!"
said Pedro.

"Rebecca, you mustn't throw the ball into the goal," said Danny.

Daddy Pig came.

"Let's start again," he said. "You must KICK the ball into the goal. You mustn't throw it."

Richard Rabbit had the ball. He ran and ran. Then, he kicked it into Pedro's goal!

"Great!" said Danny Dog.

"That's not right,"
said Peppa.

"The boys kicked the ball
into THEIR goal!" said
Daddy Pig. "They must
kick it into the girls' goal."

"Daddy is right," said Peppa. "Let's start again!"

"Yes," said all the friends.

Peppa and her friends loved football!

Activities

The key below describes the skills practiced in each activity.

Spelling and writing

Reading

Speaking

Critical thinking

Preparation for the Cambridge Young Learners exams

Match the words to the pictures.

1 Rebecca Rabbit

2 Danny Dog

3 Suzy Sheep

4 Pedro Pony

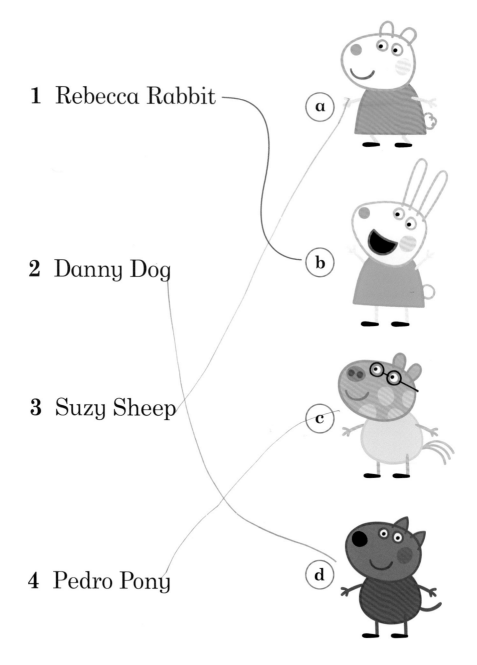

2 Find the words.

Danny
goal
Pedro
goalkeeper
teams

DokDannyglagoalcpjgoalkeeperdibpedrouslteamszhr

3 Circle the correct answers.

1 Who played tennis?

a Peppa and Rebecca Rabbit played tennis.

b Peppa and Suzy Sheep played tennis.

2 Who hit the ball to Peppa?

a Suzy hit the ball to Peppa.

b George hit the ball to Peppa.

3 Who hit the ball to Suzy?

a Rebecca hit the ball to Suzy.

b Peppa hit the ball to Suzy.

4 **Circle the correct words.**

George wanted to play tennis, too.

"You can't play tennis, George," said Peppa, "but you can get the ball for me and Suzy."

8   9

1 George **was** / **was not** happy.

2 George wanted to play
football, / **tennis,** too.

3 "You **can** / **can't** play tennis,
George," said Peppa.

4 "But you can get the
tennis / **ball** for me and Suzy."

5 George did not love
tennis. / **football.**

5 Look and read. Write *yes* or *no*.

Peppa and Suzy loved
playing tennis.

"Get the ball, George!"
said Peppa.

George had to get the ball.
He ran and ran.

George did not love tennis.

10   11

1 Peppa loved playing tennis.   yes

2 Suzy loved playing tennis.   yes

3 "Get the ball, George!"
said Suzy.   no

4 George had to run
and run for the ball.   yes

5 George loved tennis.   no

6 **Read the sentences and circle the correct words.** 📖 ✺

1 Peppa and Suzy Sheep played tennis. George . . . to play, too.
   a wanting
   b wanted

2 "You can't . . . tennis, George," said Peppa.
   a play
   b playing

3 Peppa and Suzy loved . . . tennis.
   a playing
   b played

4 George had to . . . the ball.
   a getting
   b get

7 **Look at the letters.**
Write the words.

1   (m e c a)

Peppa's friends .... came ....

2   (n t e d w a)

They .... to play, too.

3   (l y p a)

"We can .... football!"
said Danny Dog.

4   (d a i s)

"Great!" the children ....

5   (v e d o l)

Peppa and her friends
.... football!

8 **Complete the sentences.**
Write a—d.

1 The friends were in ....d........

2 There was a boys' ....

3 Pedro Pony was the
   goalkeeper for ....

4 Rebecca Rabbit was
   the goalkeeper for ....

> **a** the girls' team.
>
> **b** team.
>
> **c** the boys' team.
>
> **d** teams.

Ask and answer the questions with a friend.

Richard Rabbit got
the ball. He ran and ran.

He kicked the ball past
Peppa and Suzy . . .

16   17

1

> *Who got the ball?*

> *Richard Rabbit got the ball.*

2 What did Richard do?

3 Who kicked the ball?

4 Where did the ball go?

Circle the correct pictures.

1 Which ball did the friends kick?

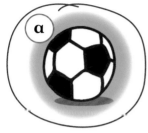

2 Who kicked the ball first?

 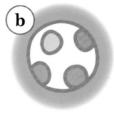

3 Who was the goalkeeper?

4 Who was happy?

Look at the picture and read the questions. Write the answers.

Rebecca got the ball.
Then, she threw it into the goal.

"Great!" said the girls.

"You can't do that!"
said Pedro.

20   21

1 What did Rebecca get?

Rebecca got the ⎯⎯ ball ⎯⎯.

2 What did Rebecca do with the ball?

Rebecca *threw* ⎯⎯ the ball.

3 Where did the ball go?

The ball went into the *goal* ⎯⎯.

12 **Read the sentences and circle the correct words.**

1 "You can't do . . . !" said Pedro.

   (**a** that)

   b this

2 "Rebecca, you mustn't throw the ball into the goal," said . . .

   a Daddy Pig.

   b Danny.

3 "Let's . . . " said Daddy Pig.

   a kick the ball,

   b start again,

4 "You must KICK the ball into the . . . You mustn't throw it."

   a goal.

   b goalkeeper.

13 Find the words. 📖

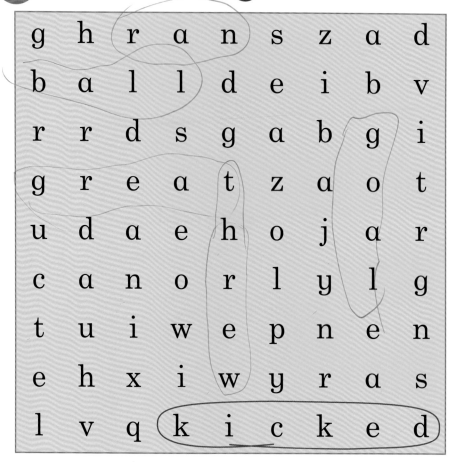

g	h	r	a	n	s	z	a	d
b	a	l	l	d	e	i	b	v
r	r	d	s	g	a	b	g	i
g	r	e	a	t	z	a	o	t
u	d	a	e	h	o	j	a	r
c	a	n	o	r	l	y	l	g
t	u	i	w	e	p	n	e	n
e	h	x	i	w	y	r	a	s
l	v	q	k	i	c	k	e	d

kicked   threw   ran

great   goal   ball

14 **Write the sentences.**

1 (must) (You) (KICK) (into)
(the goal) (the ball) (.)

You must KICK the ball
into the goal.

2 (throw) (You) (the ball) (mustn't) (.)

....

....

3 (into) (goal) (Richard) (kicked)
(the ball) (Pedro's) (!)

....

....

15 Write *must* or *mustn't*.

1  The girls' team
   ___mustn't___ throw
   the ball into the goal.

2  The boys' team
   _____ kick the
   ball into THEIR goal.

3  The boys _____
   kick the ball into the
   girls' goal.

4  The girls _____
   kick the ball into the
   boys' goal.

5  Rebecca _____
   stop the boys' ball.

Write the missing letters.

ee   bb   ee   nn   ll

1  Suzy Sh _e_ _e_ p

2  te _nn_ is

3  ba _ll_

4  goalk _ee_ per

5  Rebecca Ra _bb_ it

17 **Work with a friend. You are Peppa. Your friend is Suzy. Ask and answer the questions.**

1

> Do you like playing tennis and football?

> I like playing tennis, but I love football!

2 Do you play football with your friends?

3 What games do you play with your friends?

Level 2

 **The Gingerbread Man**	 **Sly Fox and Red Hen**	 **The Monster Next Door**	 **Wild Animals**	**Little Red Riding Hood**
978-0-241-25442-4 ☐	978-0-241-25443-1 ☐	978-0-241-25444-8 ☐	978-0-241-25445-5 ☐	978-0-241-25446-2 ☐
 **Dinosaurs**	 **Topsy and Tim The Big Race**	 **Goes to the Treehouse**	 **Sports Day**	**Going on a Picnic**
978-0-241-25447-9 ☐	978-0-241-25448-6 ☐	978-0-241-25449-3 ☐	978-0-241-26222-1 ☐	978-0-241-26221-4 ☐
Peter Rabbit and the Angry Owl	 **Superhero Max**	 **We Can Help!**	 **Daddy Pig's New Van**	 **School Trip**
978-0-241-28369-1 ☐	978-0-241-28368-4 ☐	978-0-241-28367-7 ☐	978-0-241-28371-4 ☐	978-0-241-28372-1 ☐
 **The Peter Rabbit Club**	 **Daddy Pig's Office**	 **Spring is Here!**	 **Great Trains**	 **Hungry Animals**
978-0-241-29811-4 ☐	978-0-241-29814-5 ☐	978-0-241-29809-1 ☐	978-0-241-29808-4 ☐	978-0-241-29844-2 ☐
Playing Football	 **In a Plane**	 **Mountains**	 **Grimlock Stops the Decepticons**	
978-0-241-31947-5 ☐	978-0-241-31945-1 ☐	978-0-241-31948-2 ☐	978-0-241-31954-3 ☐	

Now you're ready for Level 3!